I.S.B.N. 0 85079 115 4

 GILES

SUNDAY EXPRESS & DAILY EXPRESS CARTOONS

Thirty-fifth Series

D1438299

A DAILY EXPRESS PUBLICATION

Printed by Purnell and Sons, Ltd., Paulton (Bristol) and London

£1.35

to all lovers of
grandmas, cats, airdales,
poeople, and so forth,
i thuroughly recommend
this book.
　　on the other hand
　if you're looking for

something to make you
laugh i thuroughly
recommend you buy
something else.
giles junor

"Mind you, there's a lot to be said for <u>not</u> marrying a ravishing beauty like Anna Ford"

Sunday Express, July 13th, 1980

"I'll bet the Royal Grandma doesn't start her birthday celebrations with a large Guinness for breakfast"

Daily Express, July 15th, 1980

"Providing the Russians are jolly good sports and don't drop one on us first"

Daily Express, July 17th, 1980

"Comrade Ivan wants to know if it's true the Iron Lady's ordered the British Leyland

brass band touring Japan to commit hara-kiri if they don't win?"

Sunday Express, July 20th, 1980

"No! You're not having one"

Daily Express, July 22nd, 1980

"Harold wrote to that witch who claims she brought the good weather and said 'rubbish' "

(White witch casts good-weather spell for holidays)

Daily Express, July 24th, 1980

"Who wrote to Lord Matthews and nominated me for first of the chops?"

Sunday Express, July 27th, 1980

"Reggie got himself into the fool outfit, let Reggie get himself out"

Sunday Express, August 10th, 1980

"Princess Anne is right — one cannot use the same words when opening a new hospital
as one uses on a horse"

Daily Express, August 12th, 1980

"Willie made up his mind he would only buy British-built cars — that was in 1932"

Sunday Express, August 17th, 1980

"She says we made Dunkirk in 1940, so we can make it again to pick up her sister, Florrie"

Daily Express, August 19th, 1980

"I haven't the heart to tell them their Tibby's had six lovely little kittens"

Daily Express, August 21st, 1980

"Hallo, Kinlay — the London office got your message that you are still stuck in a traffic jam in Zeebrugge"

Sunday Express, August 24th, 1980

"Hi, Dad — want to see some erotic Polaroids of you dancing at the Carnival before Mum sees them?"

Daily Express, August 26th, 1980

"Not exactly a Centenary celebration — Harry asked Heyhoe if she ever played against W. G. Grace"

Daily Express, August 28th, 1980

"Dad read the Health Education Council handout—'Relieve the stress and tension of modern life, go by bike' "

Sunday Express, August 31st, 1980

"Here comes the imported Italian chimps who are replacing us — in a Japanese car!"

Daily Express, September 2nd, 1980

"I can't, at short notice, think of any men's jobs women aren't working at"

Daily Express, September 4th, 1980

"Your wife's arrived with the car Sir—to save you a tiring journey back after a hard week at the Conference"

Daily Express, September 6th, 1980

"One thing about moving 'Match of the Day' to Sunday — it gets 'em home earlier for lunch"

Sunday Express, September 7th, 1980

" 'Ere! They've pinched our birds!"

Daily Express, September 11th, 1980

"Daddy's done it again—'if they gave medals for peeling spuds he'd have been
the most decorated ERK in Biggin Hill' "

Sunday Express, September 14th, 1980

"The City up-train will be its usual 25 minutes late, but the new £37 million flier
hopes to knock 20 minutes off the London-to-Glasgow time"

Daily Express, September 18th, 1980

"If that spanner lands on Grandma's nut you'll get more than a nuclear explosion"

(Spanner in works starts US nuclear blaze)

Sunday Express, September 21st, 1980

"We're poker dicing for who takes HRH the first revealing instalment of 'Philip'
in the Daily Express, Your Majesty"

Daily Express, September 23rd, 1980

"If we haven't got any spectators who threw that bleedin' bottle?"

(Spectators banned from West Ham match)

Sunday Express, September 28th, 1980

"Let's have a clean fight, keep your punches up, and if you win get the hell out of it before the fans kill you!"

(Wembly boxing fans invade ring after result)

Daily Express, September 30th, 1980

"They're not Golden Delicious—I saw her going over the wall of his Lordship's orchard this morning"

Sunday Express, October 5th, 1980

"I don't think the boss is going to like you coming to work on the new 'fare-paying passenger on schoolbuses' scheme"

Daily Express, October 7th, 1980

"A very nice lady saw your Mini Metro outside, and asked me if I'd like to do a straight swop"

Daily Express, October 9th, 1980

"Do you ever wonder who wrote their scripts?"

Sunday Express, October 12th, 1980

"Angela Rippon says she often feels like saying it, Sir!"

(There are times when I want to say sod it . . . Angela Rippon)

Daily Express, October 14th, 1980

"And no pincha da bottoms!"

(Rome tidies up for the Queen's visit)

Daily Express, October 16th, 1980

"You, you and you—in here. You, you and you—hold on! They didn't tell us they were sending any from Holloway"

Sunday Express, October 19th, 1980

"Miss Potter in History taught us all they did was land over here and build good roads"

Daily Express, October 21st, 1980

" 'We can't make a cup of tea like they do in the Scrubs' "

Daily Express, October 23rd, 1980

"Ah! Pte. Smilby, went in for flogging a couple of army trucks I believe. Welcome home"

Sunday Express, October 26th, 1980

"Excuse me, Sir"

(Whitehall begins biggest mole hunt)

Daily Express, October 28th, 1980

"Well I'm damned — so they have!"

(Rugby club de-skirts woman police constable)

Sunday Express, November 2nd, 1980

" 'Ullo, looks like their having one of their room inspections"

Daily Express, November 6th, 1980

"Reagan's been elected President for nearly a week and he hasn't dropped it yet — that's £1 you owe me"

Sunday Express, November 9th, 1980

"One or two of them must have slipped harness now and then!"

Daily Express, November 11th, 1980

"I know the feeling, mate"

Daily Express, November 13th, 1980

"Children! Grandma's had enough playing Black Rod — open the door!"

(Black Rod banned from House of Commons)

Sunday Express, November 16th, 1980

"I don't think Chalkie liked the caretaker offering him a few hours overtime cleaning the washrooms"

Daily Express, November 20th, 1980

"She won't pay out on this Kristin shooting JR — she says she dozed off when they showed who dunnit"

Sunday Express, November 23rd, 1980

"The boys wish someone would put a bullet in Sue Ellen, Miss Ellie and all the bloody rest of them"

Daily Express, November 25th, 1980

"He'll get every ounce out of you now he's got to cough up this extra cash"

Daily Express, November 27th, 1980

"Farmers have a totally different attitude to bunnies when they're up for the Smithfield than they have back home"

Daily Express, December 2nd, 1980

"I know another member of the environment they want to arm—the Christmas fairy in Santa's Grotto at Harridges"

Daily Express, December 4th, 1980

"Some of us are not averse to violating the only on a Saturday rule"

Sunday Express, December 7th, 1980

"Whoever heard of Three Kings from the East with heads bald as pickled onions, Miss Sinclair?"

Daily Express, December 11th, 1980

"I'm ever so sorry — Horace hasn't heard 'We Wish You A Merry Christmas' played on a bugle before"

Sunday Express, December 14th, 1980

"Elizabeth! You've been at the cooking sherry again"

Daily Express, December 16th, 1980

"Lady, you've played it 93 times — are you going to buy the bloody thing or not?"

Daily Express, December 18th, 1980

"You've bought Grandma a WHAT for Christmas?"

Sunday Express, December 21st, 1980

"You'll never win Mastermind if you use naughty words like that"

(Taxi driver wins "Mastermind" title)

Daily Express, December 23rd, 1980

" 'Soon as the shops open after Christmas back goes that damn parrot'. Not so, says the parrot"

Sunday Express, December 28th, 1980

"As long as you share his great British passion for sailing, its beauty and its horizons —
you should have a reasonably happy marriage"

Sunday Express, January 4th, 1981

"I've passed your message to the Editor, Sir—and one from me for sending me on this story"

(Prince Charles wishes Fleet Street editors a nasty New Year)

Daily Express, January 6th, 1981

"A couple of gross of each in case they talk him into buying it"

Daily Express, January 8th, 1981

"Giving the Police extra powers doesn't entitle their new copper boyfriends to monopolise my electric Highway Patrol!"

Sunday Express, January 11th, 1981

"Good morning — happy Harrods shoppers on the right, Boat Show sun-stroke cases on the left"

(Punch-up at Harrods sale)

Daily Express, January 13th, 1981

"Yes, there are a lot of little comforts I shall miss when we go back to the Scrubs"

Daily Express, January 15th, 1981

"Which of you told the Press Lady Diana is staying with us for the weekend?"

Sunday Express, January 18th, 1981

"We sent the man next door a note saying we're holding his son hostage,
and he sent one back saying 'Thanks'"

Daily Express, January 22nd, 1981

"Murdoch's uplifted your Times, Daddy — Mona Lisa on page three!"

Sunday Express, January 25th, 1981

"Before you start on about your new-found powers to sack PMs — eat your cornflakes and get off to work"

Daily Express, January 27th, 1981

"That'll be my hired man come to give me a lift home with me heavy pension"

Daily Express, January 29th, 1981

" 'Good morning, Yellow Peril' to the foreman isn't going to enhance your chances of promotion"

Sunday Express, February 1st, 1981

"I think the possibility of us being asked back when we leave is now nil"

Daily Express, February 3rd, 1981

"They've read about that post office cat who scared off those raiders"

Daily Express, February 5th, 1981

"That reminds me — you still owe me for the ring"

Daily Express, February 10th, 1981

"If Cruft's gave an award for the best retriever on my estate, we know who'd
be supreme champion, eh, Dodger?"

Sunday Express, February 15th, 1981

"No Ursula, Chia-Chia is not going to Washington to be mated with Mrs Thatcher —
Mrs Thatcher is going to Washington to be matey with President Reagan!"

Daily Express, February 17th, 1981

"We're in enough trouble photo-copying their music, without you collecting royalties
under the name of Beethoven"

Daily Express, February 19th, 1981

"Anything they can do we can do better!"

(Oxford crew sign up girl cox)

Sunday Express, February 22nd, 1981

"If you wish to remain a permanent member of this family — no politics or religion!"

Daily Express, February 24th, 1981

"Now I've seen everything—biggest old Red in the district wearing a buttonhole for the 'appy couple!"

Daily Express, February 26th, 1981

"I cannot believe Lady Diana does not like riding!"

Sunday Express, March 1st, 1981

"The boss ventured on the shop floor like the Japs — and got 'Shaddup You Face' over the intercom"

Daily Express, March 3rd, 1981

"Ullo, there — 'The best laid schemes o' mice an' men gang aft a-gley' as you say back in the U.K.!"

Sunday Express, March 8th, 1981

"Yes lady, business as usual — beheading times nine to six, feeding times 11.30 and 4.30"

Daily Express, March 10th, 1981

"Ah! The good news, Vera—Thatcher's invited Reagan to build a germ warfare station half a mile up the road"

Daily Express, March 12th, 1981

"In the olden days it would have been the Tower of London royal knacker's yard for you, mate"

Sunday Express, March 15th, 1981

"Don't book me for calling him a cheat . . . I called him a thief"

Daily Express, March 17th, 1981

"I fell off 15 times!"

Daily Express, March 19th, 1981

"Oh dear — I forgot to tell him we don't alter the clocks until next week"

Sunday Express, March 22nd, 1981

"If a man calls at the door and says his name's Egon Ronay and wants to try your mum's food, don't let him in"

Daily Express, March 24th, 1981

"I don't think there'll be much trouble kidnapping him — it's whether you'll get anything for him"

Daily Express, March 26th, 1981

"Of course I love your Mummy, I simply said why doesn't your Mummy
go and see her Mummy on Mother's Day"

Sunday Express, March 29th, 1981

"Fred loves his Sunday marathons — but try asking him to take the dog to the end of the road!"

Daily Express, March 31st, 1981

"One other thing, Barker — it is not customary for Eton scholars' Maters
to chastise the Master every time he has occasion to admonish their sons"

Daily Express, April 2nd, 1981

"Hold it, Dad! Attila the Hun's just laid another egg"

Sunday Express, April 5th, 1981

"Dad, what comments did you let Grandma add on the bottom of that census form?"

Daily Express, April 7th, 1981

"You on cannabis, or something?"

Daily Express, April 9th, 1981

"Do you still want to buy one to help with our petrol economy?"

Sunday Express, April 12th, 1981

"Julie — you know your Easter bonnet —"

Sunday Express, April 19th, 1981

"George sayeth: 'Time-and-a-half plus danger money', or thine fair daughter hath had it"

Daily Express, April 23rd, 1981

"I thought you might have put up a prayer of thanksgiving for the salvation of poor Mr. Biggs"

Sunday Express, April 26th, 1981

"If the zoos do have to close because of lack of funds I shall miss the entertainment"

Daily Express, April 28th, 1981

"Just until he makes his mind up"

Daily Express, April 30th, 1981

"You ain't going to marry us dressed like that?"

Sunday Express, May 3rd, 1981

"There's only one more Bank Holiday this month for a long weekend on the boat"

Daily Express, May 5th, 1981

"Talking of cheque book journalism, do you think the Editor would object to us taking that cab?"

Daily Express, May 7th, 1981

"Fleet Street will give a bomb for this tape of what dad said when Aunt Florrie
phoned to say they were all coming to tea"

Sunday Express, May 10th, 1981

"Slipping Sir Hugh Casson a couple of quid to get you a good Press could constitute chequebook journalism"

Daily Express, May 12th, 1981

"We can have our disco here tonight — there's nothing on TV except the Cup Final"

Daily Express, May 14th, 1981

"One can't start too early"

Sunday Express, May 17th, 1981

"I think Sir overheard your constructive suggestion about where the first Navy cuts should fall"

Daily Express, May 19th, 1981

"Control to freight—police check—knock off 'Scotland the Brave' on the bagpipes"

(The F.A. banned Scottish fans from the 1981 British Championships)

Daily Express, May 21st, 1981

"Not in the wildest stretches of the imagination can I picture your Grandma wearing them in the 1920's"

Sunday Express, May 24th, 1981

"George! The President of the Show has banned alcohol — like Wembley!"

Daily Express, May 26th, 1981

"Your invitation to The Wedding's come, Maam. Please let 'em know if you wish to go by glass wedding coach or open landau"

Daily Express, May 28th, 1981

"Patricia! No Lester Piggott tactics, please!"

(Piggott fined for whipping jockey)

Sunday Express, May 31st, 1981

"Maybe if you'd let me give 'im one when he set light to his first teddy bear . . . "

Daily Express, June 2nd, 1981

"Pass the rope, Carmen — we are about to retrieve what we lost on the Derby yesterday"

Daily Express, June 4th, 1981

"Our Malcolm wanted to see Venus and Helen of Troy but we couldn't get him a passport"

(Civil Servants strike delayed issue of passports)

Sunday Express, June 7th, 1981

"I'm afraid Ching-Ching hasn't been sitting around pining while you've been foot-loosing it in the States"

Daily Express, June 9th, 1981

"Here we go again — every time BP sticks the price up, it's: Carol! Have you seen the pony?"

Daily Express, June 11th, 1981

"Coarse fishing starts Tuesday — just two days to finish painting the house, finish building the shed . . ."

Sunday Express, June 14th, 1981

"Two other things they're not going to like — your damn radio and cooking their flamingoes for breakfast"

(German students invade Palace gardens)

Daily Express, June 25th, 1981

"Ahoy! Before you go — I want a word with one of you about my daughter!"

Sunday Express, June 28th, 1981

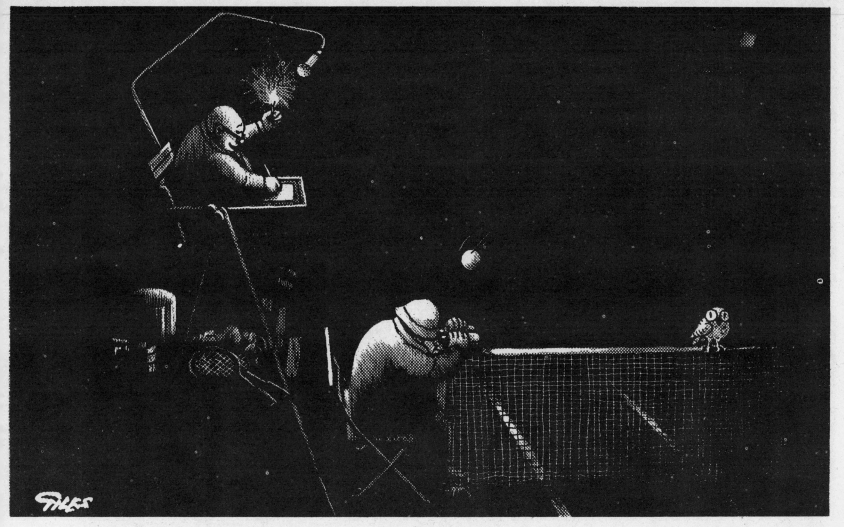

"At the risk of being bombarded with toilet rolls from the crowd, poor visibility prevents further play"

Daily Express, July 2nd, 1981

"Too much sitting on their backsides watching Wimbledon, that's their trouble"

Sunday Express, July 5th, 1981